THE Panzerkampfwa AT WAR

CW00394340

Text by Michael Jerchel & Waldemar Trojca
Color Plates by A.Wrobel

CONCORD
PUBLICATIONS COMPANY

We welcome authors who can help
expand our range of books. If you
would like to submit material,
please feel free to contract us.

We are always on the look-out for new,
unpublished photos for this series.
If you have photos or slides or
information you feel may be useful to
future volumes, please send them to us
for possible future publication.
Full photo credits will be given upon
publication.

ISBN 962-361-614-7

printed in Hong Kong

Dedication
This book is dedicated to Randolph Kugler.

Acknowledgments
The authors would like to express their sincere thanks to Oberst a.D.
Wenck, Dr. La Speranza, Michael Foedrowitz, Uwe Remmers, Uwe
Schnellbacher, Robert Michulec and Michael Green for providing
photographs and other material for this book. Special thanks are due to
Holger Veh and the Motor-Technica-Museum in Bad Oeynhausen. A
million thanks are due to Horst and Holger Beiersdorf of the
Garnisionsmuseum Celle for their generous help and support and for
providing additional photographs.
Special thanks are due to Randolph Kugler for providing material and
information about the Tauchpanzer III. As without all of them, this book
would not have been possible.

Introduction

In 1934 military demands, especially those made by Guderian, called for and led to the development of a 15-ton tank, to be armed with a yet undisclosed "armor piercing armament and coaxially mounted machine gun" (the later Panzerkampfwagen III), and a support tank, the "Bataillonsführerwagen (B.W.)" or battalion commander's vehicle (later to become the Pz.Kpfw. IV).

Involved in the developmental program under the control of WaPrÜf 6 for the 15-ton tank, launched in early 1935, were Daimler-Benz AG, MAN, Friedrich Krupp AG and Rheinmetall-Borsig. Finally the vehicle was to be designed to carry a 3.7cm Kampfwagenkanone (tank gun) as main armament (with the possibility to fit a larger caliber gun at a later stage), plus a 7.92mm MG34 machine gun (minimum) in the gun mantlet as secondary weapon and one further MG34 mounted in the hull. The vehicle itself was codenamed "Versuchskraftfahrzeug (Vers.Kfz.) 619" (trial vehicle) and later on "Zugführerwagen" (platoon leader's vehicle), also sometimes referred to as the "mittlerer traktor" (medium tractor), which was finally to become the Panzerkampfwagen (Pz.Kpfw.) III (Sd.Kfz. 141).

The First of Many

Ausführung A

In 1936, competing vehicles of Daimler-Benz (known as 1/ZW), MAN and Henschel were ready for trials which were carried out at Kummersdorf and Ulm until 1937. Despite the trials still going on, Heereswaffenamt ordered Daimler-Benz at Marienfelde to produce a pre-series (0-Serie) of the Pz.Kpfw. III.

In May 1937, five of the Pz.Kpfw. III Ausführung (Ausf.) A became available, a further batch of ten vehicles were built until the end of 1937 (chassis no. 60101 to 60110). There are certain indications that only 8 of the Ausf. A models received a turret with armament. The chassis of this type was designated 1/ZW, ZW standing for Zugführerwagen (platoon leader's vehicle).

The Pz.Kpfw. III Ausf. A was protected by 14.5mm thick armor on the chassis and 10mm of armor on the turret, which was sufficient to withstand armor piercing ammunition of anti-tank rifles then in service. The armament consisted of a 3.7cm Kampfwagenkanone (KwK) L/46.5 main gun, two 7.92mm MG34 machine guns as secondary armament mounted coaxially in the gun mantlet, and a further MG34 in a ball bearing mount, to the right hand side in the front plate of the superstructure. The turret was made by Rheinmetall-Borsig and was operated manually, traversing 360 degrees, with maximum depression of -10 degrees to maximum elevation of +20 degrees for the main gun. The main gun was aimed by the gunner under use of the TZF-5a scope. The crew consisted of a driver, radio operator/MG gunner (both in the superstructure), loader, gunner and

tank commander (in the turret). There was a FuG 5 radio set installed.

The Ausf. A had five large road wheels with individual coil springs, and two large return rollers per side; the drive sprocket was installed at the front, the idler wheel at the rear. The type of track used was designated Kgs 6100/360/120, it was 36cm wide and 340cm long. The vehicle was powered by a V12-cylinder Maybach HL 108TR petrol engine developing 250 PS (at 3,000 rpm), installed in the rear compartment of the hull, allowing the 15,400kg weighing vehicle a maximum speed of up to 32km/hr on even ground. The fuel tanks with a capacity of 300 liters allowed a maximum range of 165km on roads and approximately 95km cross country.

Ausführung B

Next on delivery in 1937 was the Ausführung B, of which 15 vehicles (chassis no. 60201 to 60215) were built. This version introduced a change in the suspension, which consisted of a bogie/leaf spring combination. There were two leaf springs on two identical bogie trucks, which had four small road wheels each, and three return rollers per side, with the drive sprocket at the front and idler at the rear. The chassis was designated 2/ZW. The exhaust system and the driver's vision port were modified, the track length was reduced to 320cm, maximum speed now was 35km/hr with a combat weight of 15,900kg. The new commander's cupola on the turret was identical to that used on the Pz.Kpfw. IV Ausf. A. Between 1937 and 1938, five Ausf. B chassis were used for the 0-series of the Sturmgeschütz III. However, until 1940 all Ausf. B were withdrawn from front line service and transferred to training units.

Ausführung C

This was followed by Ausführung C, of which 15 vehicles were built (chassis No. 60301 to 60315) in June 1937 to January 1938, with the chassis of this type being designated 3a/ZW. It had a rearranged bogie/leaf spring type suspension, there were now three leaf springs for the two bogie trucks per side, with hydraulic shock absorbers. Altogether, there were eight small road wheels and three return rollers mounted per side. It had an improved steering mechanism and the combat weight increased to 16,000kg.

Ausführung D

Last of the trial series was the Ausführung D, built in two groups of 15 vehicles in total (chassis no. 60221 to 60225 and 60316 to 60340) between January and June 1938, with the chassis being designated 3b/ZW. Although the suspension was similar to the one used on the Ausf. C, the front and rear spring were angled and the hydraulic shock absorbers relocated towards the outer ends of the vehicle. Presumably with the second group, the armor had been increased to 30mm on the hull, resulting in a higher combat weight of 19,800kg. The suspension system used so far proved to be impractical and not suitable for combat use, none was accepted for large scale series production.

Large Scale Series Production Vehicles

Ausführung E

The first large scale series production version was the Pz.Kpfw. III Ausführung E (Sd.Kfz. 141). With the chassis designated 4/ZW (or ZW 38) and the chassis no. in the

The Ausf. E was the first version to see mass production. Compared to the earlier versions, the Ausf. E had thicker armor protection all around. The increase in weight resulted in a new suspension system which consisted of six road wheels individually supported by torsion bars. This suspension design proved to be a full success and became standard to all versions of the Panzerkampfwagen III built thereafter.

An Ausf. F giving a ride to the infantry during an exercise. Although the censor has deleted the driver's vision port, the external gun mantlet shows that this is a late production Ausf. F, armed with the 5cm KwK L/42 main gun. (Archiv Trojca)

range between 60401 and 61000 (without using the range between 60501 to 60545), about 96 vehicles were built from October 1938 until October 1939. Involved in the series production were the companies ALKETT Werk Spandau, ALKETT Werk Falkensee, Daimler-Benz Werk Berlin-Marienfelde, FAMO Werk Breslau, Henschel und Sohn AG Werk Kassel (until November 1942), MAN Werk Nuernberg, Waggonfabrik Wegmann AG Werk Kassel (1937 until middle of 1942) and Maschinenfabrik Niedersachsen-Hannover (MNH) in Hannover-Linden (there are some indications that also HANOMAG and Edelstahlwerke in Hannover were involved, MIAG Werk Braunschweig was involved from 1941 to 1943).

The chassis, for the first time ever, introduced the torsion bar suspension, designed by Ferdinand Porsche. It proved to be a full success so it became standard to any version of the Panzerkampfwagen III built thereafter.

Compared to the earlier versions, the Ausf. E had 30mm thick single piece armor plates at the sides and front of the hull and superstructure, and plates of 16 and 21mm at the rear. The armor protection of the turret was 30mm all around. Further small improvements included the installation of a two part armored visor for the driver, and at the turret sides, the single doors were replaced by double doors which had vision slots and pistol ports. The armament consisted of a 3.7cm KwK L/46.5 plus three 7.92mm MG34. The Ausf. E was powered by the Maybach HL 120TR engine, delivering 300 PS, the combat weight was 19,500kg, and the maximum achievable speed was 40km/hr.

Ausführung F

Next on the assembly line was the Pz.Kpfw. III Ausführung F (Sd.Kfz. 141), of which 435 vehicles were built. The chassis was designated 5/ZW, and the chassis no. were in the range between 61001 to 61650. This version introduced armored covers on the final drive cooling air intakes on the vehicle's bow near the headlights, the brake system was improved, additional position lights were fitted, and the modified Maybach HL 120TRM engine, which although still delivered 300 PS, was built in.

Late type Ausf. F (the first 10 Ausf. E with 5cm L/42 gun were built in June 1940) and reworked Ausf. E and Ausf. F were armed with the new 5cm L/42 gun, and some reworked Ausf. E also received the armored covers on the final drive cooling air intakes, which in return makes it nearly impossible to visually distinguish the Ausf. E from Ausf. F at this later stage. A number of reworked Ausf. E/F received

30mm extra armor plates on the bow and 30mm of spaced add-on armor on the front of the superstructure. One of the last Pz.Kpfw. III Ausf. E was knocked out during the Allied landings in Normandy in June 1944.

Ausführung G

The next version built was the Pz.Kpfw. III Ausführung G (with chassis designated 6/ZW and with chassis no. ranging from 65001 to 65950). About 600 vehicles were built from the beginning of May 1940 until February 1941. The Ausf. G introduced an increased armor from 21mm to 30mm on the rear hull plate, and the smoke candle rack at the rear right received armor plating. The driver's vision sliding block was replaced by a Fahrersehklappe 30 (driver's visor port), actually a pivoted armored cover. Although some vehicles of the early production batch were still armed with the 3.7cm KwK L/46.5 gun, the majority was fitted out with the 5cm KwK38 L/42 main gun, mounted in an external mantlet of 37mm thick rounded armor. A coaxial MG34 was mounted to the right hand side of the main gun. On the roof of the turret an electrical operated ventilator was built in, located in the center and slightly offset to the right, to extract the fumes when the gun was fired.

Late Ausf. G received 30mm extra armor plates on the front plates of the bow and the superstructure, and an extra armor plate for the lower hull rear. A newly designed cast commander's cupola was fitted to late built vehicles, which was identical to the one installed on the Panzerkampfwagen IV. At the turret rear, a large stowage bin known as "Rommelkiste" (Rommelbox) was installed, becoming standard for all Pz.Kpfw. III. The Ausf. G also introduced new drive wheels and new idler wheels together with the 40cm wide tracks designated Kgs 61/400/120.

Vehicles destined to serve with the Afrika

An Ausf. G followed by several Ausf. F of the 5.Panzerdivision during the invasion of Bulgaria in early March 1941. This is one of the late production Ausf. G. Late production ones featured a new cast cupola with better armor protection. (Dr. La Speranza)

Korps, designated Pz.Kpfw. III Ausf. G (Tp, i.e. Tropen), received an improved cooling air flow by the provision of two cooling air intakes on the rear engine access hatches and better air filters. This version also introduced the ventilator covers on the engine deck hatches.

Ausführung H

The Pz.Kpfw. III Ausführung H, with the chassis designated 7/ZW (chassis no. 66001 to 68000), was built in the beginning of October 1940. The hull and superstructure were fitted with factory applied add-on armor, which gave an armor protection of 60mm in total. At the driver's station, a KFF 2 optic was built-in. The rear plate of the turret was redesigned as one piece, deleting the bulge below the commander's hatch. A rotating turret basket with floor was installed, and to cope with the extra weight of the additional armor, the chassis was modified, including the new 40cm wide tracks (Kgs 61/400/120) which replaced the 36cm wide tracks used on previous versions, new sprockets and idler wheels were also fitted, as were reshaped shock absorbers. The first return rollers were repositioned slightly forward towards the bow. With the production of the Ausf. J at hand, which was to be the major improved variant, the production of Ausf. H ceased after a little more than 400 vehicles built.

Ausführung J

The Pz.Kpfw. III Ausführung J, with the chassis designated 8/ZW (chassis no. 68001 to 69100 and 72001 to 74100), which was built from March 1941 until July 1942, incorporated improvements and changes based on combat experiences. Whereas the side armor remained 30mm thick, the armor plates of the superstructure front, the bow and the rear were now 50mm thick. The hull was lengthened, and the rear of the vehicle was redesigned, including the engine deck which received an extension to the rear. The smoke candles moved into a position below the tailplate, and a deflector shield was fitted. At the superstructure front, the Fahrersehklappe 50 vision slot replaced the previously used Fahrersehklappe 30, and the square type Kugelblende 30 machine gun mount was replaced by a ball mount Kugelblende 50 (as used with the Pz.Kpfw. IV Ausf. F). The two piece access hatches on the upper hull front for the transmission/final drives were changed to single piece hatches. The turret armor was 30mm all around, the armor of the gun mantlet was 50mm thick. The 37mm thick vision port flaps in the mantlet were replaced by 50mm armored ones.

While the Pz.Kpfw. III Ausf. J (frueh, i.e. early) still retained the 5cm KwK38 L/42 main gun, the Pz.Kpfw. III Ausf. J (spaet, i.e. late) built from December 1941 onwards received the 5cm KwK39 L/60 gun. Since the rounds of the new gun were longer, the number carried had to be reduced from 99 to 84. Vehicles with the long barreled gun received the official designation Sd.Kfz. 141/1, and after the first battles against British troops in North Africa, they soon

became known as the "Mark III special". However, as most of the parts such as drive sprockets and idler wheels were interchangeable, there was the possibility of a "mix" of parts on one vehicle, sometimes lack of spare parts of the new type led to the use of elderly ones, or, vice versa, the use of new parts on older versions, very much depending on availability.

Ausführung L

Ongoing studies seemed to lead to the fact that it was impractical to adopt the 7.5cm KwK40 main gun of the Pz.Kpfw. IV on the Pz.Kpfw. III. Until the final outcome of the trials to fit a larger caliber gun, it was decided to built an improved version, the Pz.Kpfw. III Ausführung L, with the chassis designated 9/ZW (chassis no. 74101 to 76000).

The most significant improvement was the fitting of spaced armor to the front of the superstructure and on the gun mantlet. Attachment holds were welded onto the front of the superstructure, to keep the 20mm spaced armor plate in place. Improvements concerning the engine deck included enlarged radiator access hatches, and single piece engine access hatches replaced the double hatches used on previous versions. The air intakes on these hatches were mounted parallel to the vehicle's centerline instead of, in previous case, transverse to it. The escape hatches on both sides of the hull were deleted. On the gun mantlet, a frame was attached to take on the spaced armor plate, increasing the protection here to 57mm in total. Early vehicles were delivered without the armor plate but already had the frame fitted to the mantlet. The vision ports were deleted from the turret sides. The recoil system of the 5cm KwK39 L/60 gun was changed from a coil spring to a

torsion bar mechanism, which in return led to a further reduction from 84 to 78 rounds in the ammunition stowage when compared to the Ausf. J (late).

For the Afrika Korps, a tropicalized version designated Pz.Kpfw. III Ausf. L (Tp) was built. The air intake for the engine was replaced to the inside of the engine compartment, and special oil filters were installed. There was now a large single piece engine access hatch, and larger air inlets with dust filters were installed.

Ausführung M

The Pz.Kpfw. III Ausführung M (Sd.Kfz. 141/1), with chassis designated 10/ZW (chassis no. 76101 to 77800), was the final version with the 5cm KwK gun. It was built from October 1942 until February 1943. It was originally planned (WaPrüf 6) to built about 1,000 vehicles of this version, but this number was reduced to about 250. Most were converted to Sturmgeschütz III or Pz.Kpfw. III Ausf. N.

The most significant improvement on the Ausf. M was the installation of a wading equipment. This included watertight covers on the air inlets for the engine, a water tight cover mount on the turret around the gun mantlet, and all vents, inlets and exhausts of the hull received new seals. During wading, the air for the engine was taken through the vehicle's turret. The tail boom was extended, and two hinged, rubber sealed and manually operated air outlet cover plates were provided. The exhaust pipe system was extended to the upper rear plate, where at the rear left a muffler with non return valve was located. This allowed the vehicle to wade through 1,300mm deep water obstacles, compared to the 900mm of previous versions.

The hinges of the equipment access hatches on the glacis had been relocated to the inside. The old headlights known from previous versions were deleted, and a pair of Bosch-

Presumably an Ausf. J brought up to Ausf. L standard by fitting the additional spaced armor to the front of the superstructure front and to the gun mantlet. Attachment holds were welded onto the front of the superstructure, to keep the 20mm spaced armor plate in place. A Pz.Kpfw. IV can be seen in the background. (Archiv Trojca)

lights were fitted on the fenders. The smoke candle array below the rear deck was deleted and a triple mount of electrically-fired 90mm caliber NBK smoke mortars were mounted to each side of the turret.

Most vehicles received side skirts (Seitenschürzen), on both the hull and the turret, which were subsequently also fitted to numerous Pz.Kpfw. III Ausf. L. On late vehicles, a deflector ring was added around the commander's cupola, where an air defense machine gun mount (Fliegerbeschussgeraet 41) was installed. Later it was replaced by a Fliegerbeschussgeraet 42 in 1943, which allowed to mount either an MG34 or MG42.

Ausführung N

The Pz.Kpfw. III Ausführung N appeared in late 1942, it was the final version of the Panzer III series. Early Ausf. N were based on the chassis of the Ausf. L (very few also on Ausf. J), while late vehicles were based on the chassis of the Ausf. M. As the most significant change, the 5cm KwK39 L/60 was replaced by a 7.5cm KwK37 L/24 gun, which came from early versions of the Pz.Kpfw. IV series (Ausf. A to F1). Due to the different size of the ammunition for the gun, ammunition stowage had to be changed and 64 rounds were allowed to be stored. The gun fired a highly effective high explosive round, superior to the one fired by the 5cm L/60 gun. The Ausf. N primarily served as a support tank for the Pz.Kpfw. VI Tiger I (Sd. Kfz. 181) units. For example, the sPz.Abt. 501 fighting in North Africa had the early variant of the Ausf. N based on Ausf. L chassis. Although there were different types of chassis used, it was designated 11/ZW for all, and the official designation for the vehicle was Sd.Kfz. 141/2.

The triple smoke mortar launcher on each side of the turret was standard for all vehicles of the Ausf. N. At a later stage, a number of vehicles that were returned to the factories for major overhaul or repair were also converted to the Ausf. N, and the majority of those vehicles (if not all) rebuilt in 1943 were fitted with factory applied Zimmerit anti-magnetic mine paste.

Introduced on 19th March 1943 in Ruegenwalde for the first time, late vehicles received Seitenschürzen (side skirts) on the turret and the hull, and some vehicles received a single piece commander's hatch (coming from the Pz.Kpfw. IV) instead of the two piece hatch. The installation of a Fliegerbeschussgeraet (machine gun mount) on the cupola was optional.

Special Panzerkampfwagen III

Variants
Panzerbefehlswagen III Ausf. D1

Special command tank versions were developed to provide high ranking officers with armor capable to accompany armored formations in the field, following the doctrine "commanding from the front line". The first

version, of which 30 were built between June 1938 and March 1939 (chassis no. 60341 to 60370), was the Panzerbefehlswagen (PzBefWg) III Ausf. D1, which was based on the chassis of Ausf. D, with the chassis being designated 3c/ZW. On the rear deck, a large frame antenna for the FuG 8 was installed, further equipment included a 1.4m and a 2m long whip antenna plus a telescopic radio mast (Typ P) with a maximum height of 9m. The turret was fixed to the chassis, and as disguise there was a dummy gun barrel fitted to the also fixed mantlet. For self defense, there was one MG34 installed to the right of the dummy gun in a flexible mount. The combat weight was around 20,000kg. Depending on which radio sets were used, the vehicles were designated either the Sd.Kfz. 266 (FuG 6 and FuG 2), 267 (FuG 6 and 8), or 268 (FuG 6 and 7). Other sources also list the possibility of a FuG 13 used as an alternative to the FuG 6.

Panzerbefehlswagen III Ausf. E

Next came the PzBefWg III Ausf. E which was sometimes also used by airforce (Luftwaffe) forward air controllers, and was used for the first time during the French campaign. The turret was fixed to the chassis (designated 4a/ZW) that came from the Pz.Kpfw. III Ausf. E and it was similarly equipped like the Ausf. D1. A variation of radio sets was available, among them FuG 6 (ultra short wave, frequency 27.2 to 33.3 MHz), FuG 7 (ultra short wave, frequency 42.1 to 47.8 MHz), and FuG 8 (30 W medium wave transceiver, frequency 0.83 to 3.0 MHz) or FuG 13 (ultra short wave, frequency 27.2 to 33.3 MHz), which were installed in a combination. As with Ausf. D1, depending on which types of radio sets were used, the vehicles were designated either Sd.Kfz. 266, 267 or 268.

Panzerbefehlswagen III Ausf. H

After the former variant had proven to be a success, the PzBefWg Ausf. H was built, based on the chassis (designated 7a/ZW) of the Pz.Kpfw. III Ausf. H, with chassis no. in the range from 70001 to 70145 (built from November 1940 until September 1941) and from 70146 to 70175 (built from December 1941 until January 1942). This version had 30mm armor plates bolted to the bow and the front of the superstructure, and it had the 40cm wide tracks. While early vehicles had a dummy gun representing the 3.7cm KwK L/46.5 and a dummy machine gun, this was later changed to a fake 5cm KwK L/42 gun, and at the end the dummy machine gun barrel was deleted. As with PzBefWg III Ausf. E, there was a 7.92mm MG34 machine gun in a flexible mount installed in the fixed gun mantlet. In the turret, with an opening in the turret roof covered by a hinged circular hatch, an observation sight for the commander was installed.

Panzerbefehlswagen III Ausf. J

From August till November 1942 and from May till September 1943, 185 Pz.Kpfw. III Ausf. J (early) were converted by Daimler-Benz into PzBefWg III Ausf. J. This version received spaced armor on the front of the superstructure and had a 2m star antenna for the FuG 8 fitted in an armored socket on the rear deck between the two inspection hatches. Most interestingly, early vehicles of this command version retained the original 5cm KwK38 L/42 gun, whereas the later converted vehicles had the longer barreled 5cm KwK39 L/60 - although with reduced internal ammunition stowage due to the space required by the additional radio equipment (FuG 5, FuG 7 and FuG 8).

Panzerbefehlswagen III Ausf. K

The Panzerbefehlswagen III Ausf. K

A PzBefWg III Ausf. H follows several Pz.Kpfw. III Ausf. F entering a town. As a result of combat experience in France and Poland, additional armor was bolted to the front of the hull and superstructure, and hull rear. (Archiv Trojca)

appeared in 1943 and was based on the Ausf. L. The spaced armor plate in front of the superstructure differed slightly from that used with the PzBefWg III Ausf. J, it had a smaller opening for the ball mounted machine gun and the bolts were relocated. Photographs show that the turret originated from the Pz.Kpfw. IV Ausf. F and was reworked for the new purpose. A new smaller mantlet was added to the left turret front, with the 5cm KwK39 L/60 gun offset to the right in the mantlet. The gun could be aimed and fired, although there was only a reduced number of rounds stored. A vision port with an armored cover was installed to the right of the mantlet. Two triple smoke mortars, which were also taken over from the Panzer IV series, were mounted on the turret sides. On the rear deck between the two inspection hatches, a 2m star antenna for the FuG 8 radio set was installed in an armored socket. Most, not all, were equipped with Seitenschürzen around the turret and on the hull sides. There was presumably only a small number of this final command version built.

Panzerbeobachtungswagen III

The Panzerbeobachtungswagen III (Sd.Kfz. 143), armored artillery observation vehicle, was converted from different versions of obsolete Pz.Kpfw. III and used by forward artillery observers of the self-propelled howitzer batteries of the Panzerdivisions, equipped with 15cm self-propelled howitzer Hummel and 10.5cm self-propelled howitzer Wespe. Early converted PzBeobWg III received 30mm armor plates on the front of the bow and on the rear plate, and spaced armor on the front of the superstructure. The machine gun in the front plate was deleted and gave way to a pistol port. On the turret, the gun mantlet was fixed, and a dummy gun barrel was mounted on the former coaxial machine gun position. The original gun was taken out, and a flexible machine gun mount was installed in this position. With both the ventilator and signal port relocated in the turret roof, a small opening for the retractable TBF-2 observation periscope was provided, which could be closed by a hinged armored cover. On the rear deck, a 2m star antenna for the FuG 8 was installed in a position identical to that of the PzBefWg III. Further radio equipment included the FuG 4, radio set f and radio set g. In 1943 a small number of PzBeobWg III with 5cm KwK39 L/60 gun was built.

Flammpanzer III

Commonly known as the Flammpanzer, the Pz.Kpfw. III Ausf. M (Fl) (Sd.Kfz. 141/3) was built from February till April 1943, by adaptation of the flamethrower originally used in captured Char B1bis tanks (officially designated B2 (f) by the Germans) into the turret of the Pz.Kpfw. III Ausf. M. The 100 chassis (chassis no. 77609 to 77708) used for the conversion undertaken by Wegmann Waggonfabrik in Kassel were built and delivered by MIAG in Braunschweig. In lieu of

A Tauchpanzer III Ausf. F is lifted into the water by a crane mounted on a ship used for transport, during trials at Sylt in autumn 1940. A total of 168 Tauchpanzers were converted from Pz.Kpfw. III Ausf. F, Ausf. G, Ausf. H and some PzBefWg III command tanks. (Archiv Randolf Kugler)

the main gun, a flame oil projector of 1,500mm in length and 140mm in diameter was fitted. Two large flame oil tanks with a capacity of 1,000 liters and a pump, driven by a DKW 2-stroke auxiliary engine with 3 PS delivering 15 atm pressure for the flame oil launch circuit, were installed in the hull. This allowed approximately 125 throws of 1 second duration. The maximum range for the ignited flame oil was about 60m, although the practical range was about 40m. The MG34 machine gun in the superstructure, which had a 30mm additional spaced armor plate, and the MG mounted coaxially was retained as secondary armament. However, the crew was reduced to a driver, radio operator and a commander, who worked alone in the turret. There was a FuG 5 and a FuG 2 radio installed, the combat weight was about 23,000kg.

Tauchpanzer III

For Operation "Seeloewe" (Sea Lion), the planned invasion of England, a number of tanks, including 168 Pz.Kpfw. III Ausf. F, G and H, and PzBefWg III Ausf. E, were converted between June and October 1940 to Tauchpanzer (diving tanks) III. These special tanks served with Tauchpanzer-Abteilung "A" (formed by volunteers from Panzerregiment 2 during September/October 1940) in Putlos, and with the subsequently formed Tauchpanzer-Abteilung "B" (formed by volunteers of Panzerregiment 3), Tauchpanzer-Abteilung "C" (formed from volunteers of 3. and 5.Panzerdivisions), and Tauchpanzer-Abteilung "D" (formed by volunteers of 4.Panzerdivision and Panzerlehrregiment).

All openings on the tank were sealed by rubber, fabric covers and tar. The engine air

intakes were closed by watertight rubber seals and the two exhaust stacks received non return valves. The turret ring was tightened with an inflatable rubber seal, the mantlet, the ball bearing mount in the superstructure and the commander's cupola were also made watertight by a rubber cover. Special line charges were fitted to the rubber seals which were ignited to blow off the rubber covers once the tank entered dry ground. A pump was installed to remove any water entering the tanks inside. During the underwater drive at a maximum depth of 15m (with 3m reserve), engine cooling was provided by the sea water. The air for the engine and the crew was supplied by a 18,000mm long flexible hose with a diameter of 200mm, that had a buoy installed at the other end with an approximate 1.50m long stack forming the air inlet, and later on a radio antenna was mounted on top of the stack to enable radio communication. The orientation during underwater drive was provided by a gyroscope and by radio communication with the transportation ship.

First trials were carried out in August 1940 near Emden, under support of Pionier-Lehrregiment 1 (engineer training regiment) under command of Oberstleutnant Henke. During further trials carried out at Sylt in autumn of 1940, a landing operation was conducted, involving the crane ship "Viper" (a former gun boat) and the small freighter "Hans Herbert", both fitted with a special ramp allowing the tanks to be brought into the water.

Although the landing trials worked well, due to the cancellation of Operation "Seeloewe", the Tauchpanzers of Panzerregiment 18 of 18.Panzerdivision were moved to the training area Milowitz (a number of Tauchpanzer III came to Panzerregiment 6 of 3.Panzerdivision) in March 1941. In Milowitz,

The next version built, known as the StuG III Ausf. B, had an improvement to the drive train. The later production vehicles had the new six-spoke drive sprocket and eight-spoke idler designed for the wider 40cm track. This Ausf. B is seen fighting in Russia in 1941. (Archiv Trojca)

the vehicles had been modified by replacing the flexible hose with a steel tube snorkel, this was about 3,500mm long and had a diameter of about 75mm, mounted over the commander's cupola. The air flow for the crew and the engine was now through the fighting compartment. The exhaust system was fitted with a non return valve, thus preventing exhaust fumes entering the fighting compartment in any case. In early April 1941, all Tauchpanzers of Pz.Rgt. 18 were moved to Eberswalde, where at Werbelliner Lake a diving exercise was carried out.

During the first days of June 1941, Tauchpanzers were deployed near the Bug river, and on 22nd of June 1941 at 04.45 hours, Tauchpanzer III of 2./Panzerregiment 18 (18. Panzerdivision) crossed the river Bug in a deep wading operation (the start of "Barbarossa"). After this, the tanks were used as regular tanks with 6. and 18.Panzerdivisions.

Sturminfanteriegeschütz 33

The Sturminfanteriegeschütz III (StuG), sometimes incorrectly referred to as sIG 33, was an armored infantry support weapon. Based on the 8/ZW chassis, the vehicle had 80mm armor at the front and 50mm at the sides. Its armament, the 15cm schweres Infanteriegeschütz (sIG) 33 L/11, was destined to destroy buildings in urban warfare (a forerunner of the Panzer IV based "Brummbär"). As secondary armament, an MG34 was installed to the right of the sIG 33. Presumably 24 vehicles had been built in 1942, with about 12 vehicles used in the battle of Stalingrad, where they were lost.

Bergepanzer III and minor variants

In early 1944, a number of Pz.Kpfw. III were converted to armored recovery vehicles (Bergepanzer). The turret was taken off, and the resulting space was converted by wooden boards into a cargo bay. A crane with the capacity to lift 1,000kg was installed. This version was planned to be used among Sturmgeschütz units. In March 1944, in Kummersdorf, one vehicle (chassis no. 74104) was fitted out with a cable winch with the ability to tow up to 15,000kg. A similar conversion was that of the Pionierpanzerwagen III (armored combat engineer vehicle), as these were also regular Pz.Kpfw. III Ausf. L and M which had their turrets taken off and fitted with a wooden cargo bay. To the left and right hand side of the chassis, these vehicles carried small Pionierbruecken (bridges) as well as special engineer equipment that was stowed at various places on the vehicle.

In May 1943, a small number of Pz.Kpfw. III Ausf. E, F and G were converted to Munitionspanzer III (ammunition supply vehicle) which also had their turrets taken off, and which were used in Tiger I equipped units. A small number of turretless Pz.Kpfw. III were also used as Schlepper (tractor) in artillery units. However, the turrets of the converted Pz.Kpfw. III were used as pill-box in fortifications in Italy and at the Atlantikwall in France.

On 20th October 1943, a Pz.Kpfw. III Ausf. N converted to a railroad vehicle was demonstrated to Hitler in Arys. The conversion was carried out by Saurer, but it did not enter production. In 1945 trials were launched to mount the "Wirbelwind"-turret (4 x 2cm) and the "Ostwind"-turret (1 x 3.7cm) on the chassis of the Pz.Kpfw. III. Until the end of war, this program was not finished.

Sturmgeschütz III

The chassis of the Panzerkampfwagen III was used to develop the Sturmgeschütz III, an assault gun originally designed to serve as an infantry support vehicle. Heavily armored and armed with a large caliber gun, the assault guns (or StuGs) were operated by crews of the artillery, forming the new branch Sturmartillerie. StuG IIIs were efficient weapons and used with great success not only in the tank hunter role. However, the focus of this book is on the Pz.Kpfw. III and a thorough and in depth coverage of the StuG III will perhaps be given in a later Concord book. Therefore, only a brief look can be taken at the most common point, the use of the chassis of the Pz.Kpfw. III for the StuG III series.

The first five vehicles, of which the first was available for trials in 1937, were known as the "0-series" and based on the chassis of the

By Hitler's request, further improvements were made to the StuG III, with the increase in armor protection and the mounting of the 7.5cm StuK40 gun. This frontal view of an Ausf. F with the StuK40 L/43 gun shows the old style tow shackles and cover headlights carried over from the Ausf. E. (Archiv Trojca)

Pz.Kpfw. III Ausf. B (chassis designated 2/ZW). Although they were armed with the 7.5cm Sturmkanone (StuK) L/24, they were only used for trials and later for training.

The first production variant was the StuG III Ausf. A (Sd.Kfz. 142), which used the 5/ZW chassis that was equivalent to the chassis of the Pz.Kpfw. III Ausf. F.

Built on the 7/ZW chassis (derived from that of the Pz.Kpfw. III Ausf. H) were the StuG III Ausf. B (Sd.Kfz. 142), Ausf. C, Ausf. D and Ausf. E. These versions had the 7.5cm StuK37 L/24 short barreled gun.

The StuG III Ausf. F was practically an upgunned version of the Ausf. E, introducing the 7.5cm StuK40 L/43 in the early variant, while the late version mounted the 7.5cm StuK40 L/48.

The StuG III Ausf. F/8 (Sd.Kfz. 142/1) was based on the slightly longer 8/ZW chassis (derived from the chassis of the Pz.Kpfw. III Ausf. J), which was also used for the StuG III Ausf. G. Both versions were armed with the long barreled 7.5cm StuK40 L/48. A number of StuG III Ausf. G were built under use of the original chassis intended to be built as Pz.Kpfw. III Ausf. M.

Into Battle - the Pz.Kpfw. III at War

The invasion of the Sudetenland in autumn of 1938 saw the participation of the 1. and 2.Panzerdivisions (Pz.Kpfw. III Ausf. A and B), but the first true wartime engagements for the Pz.Kpfw. III was the war against Poland in September 1939. The total number involved were 86 Pz.Kpfw. III (other sources stated 98) and 20 to 25 PzBefWg III Ausf. D1, which were used in Panzerlehrbataillon of 3.Panzerdivision (part of XIXth Panzerkorps Heeresgruppe Nord, commanded by General Heinz Guderian), and in 1.Panzerdivision of Heeresgruppe Sued. Information about losses are sparse, but the probable number of Pz.Kpfw. III lost in action was not more than 8 vehicles in total. On 22nd September 1939 at Brest, where Soviet T-26 that had invaded Poland from the east on 17th September 1939 paraded for Guderian, the rather new design of the Pz.Kpfw. III impressed the Russians. It was during this parade that Soviet agents photographed and collected information about this vehicle, and these information were send to Kharkov in October 1939 for further examination.

At the beginning of the war against France (including Belgium and the Netherlands) in May 1940, the German Army had about 380 Pz.Kpfw. III Ausf. A to E and about 60 to 70 PzBefWg III, these were used primarily as spearheads to breakthrough French lines. For example, Panzerregiments 1 and 2 of 1.Panzerdivision had 62 Pz.Kpfw. III and 36 Pz.Kpfw. IV, plus 15 PzBefWg III, at their disposal. The first German tank in the Belgian town of St. Vith was a Pz.Kpfw. III Ausf. E of Panzerregiment 31/5.Panzerdivision. On 10th June 1940, Pz.Kpfw. III of Panzerregiment 25/7.Panzerdivision reached the beaches of the Atlantic.

When the Balkans war broke out in April 1941, the Pz.Kpfw. III fought again (among others with 2., 5., 8. and 11.Panzerdivisions), although this time heavy ground and bad road conditions seemed to be the most capable enemy, as several were lost in accidents.

When the Soviet Union was invaded by the Wehrmacht on 22 June 1941, about 1,440 Pz.Kpfw. III of all versions were available at the participating Panzerdivisions. In 1942 the first tanks to reach Rostow and Woronez were Pz.Kpfw. III, and it was a Pz.Kpfw. III Ausf. J of 23.Panzerdivision being the first tank to reach the bank of the river Volga in Stalingrad - where a great number of Pzkpw III were to be lost.

The Deutsche Afrika Korps (DAK) arrived in Africa in early 1941, and the only unit with tanks was Panzerregiment 5/5.Leicht Afrika Division (mech.), before Panzerregiment 8/15.Panzerdivision was fully assembled. On 30 March 1941 at Marsa el Brega, it was the Pz.Kpfw. III that battled the dug-in tanks of the British 4 RTR and 7 RTR, then spearheading towards Tobruk. The German offensive stopped and fighting was intense, as (for example) on 30th of April 1941, 2./Panzerregiment 5 of 5.Leicht Afrika Division had 36 Pz.Kpfw. III Ausf. E and F - after 3 days of fighting, there were only 12 left (another 14 were repaired later). In the summer of 1941, the first new Pz.Kpfw. III with 5cm gun arrived, helping to stop the Allied counteroffensive "Operation Battleaxe" in June 1941 near Fort Capuzzo and the Halfaya Pass. In August 1941, 5.Leicht Afrika Division was renamed 21.Panzerdivision. In May 1942, the first Pz.Kpfw. III Ausf. J with the 5cm KwK39 L/60 gun arrived in Africa and saw action at the Gazhala line. And during the offensive around Tobruk in June 1942, it became obvious that the new 5cm L/60 gun was more effective than the British 2-pounders: Pz.Kpfw. III Ausf. J knocked out British A10, A13 and "Matilda" Mk.2s at long distance beyond the range of the British tank guns. It was there, that the new Pz.Kpfw. III Ausf. J L/60 became known as the "Mark III Special" to the British soldiers. At the final stage after the US had landed in North Africa, the DAK received a small number of Pz.Kpfw. III Ausf. M, and serving with the Pz.Kpfw. VI "Tiger" tanks of schwere Panzerabteilung 501 were several Pz.Kpfw. III Ausf. N (early). On 12th May 1943, the DAK surrendered.

In September 1942, the Pz.Kpfw. III of 7.Panzerdivision drove off the Allied landing at Dieppe, and in November 1942 they participated in the invasion of southern France (Vichy-France).

In the Soviet Union, the Pz.Kpfw. III of 1.SS-Panzerkorps fought at Kharkov with great success during February and March 1943.

In the beginning of 1944, the Pz.Kpfw. III were slowly withdrawn from first line front units, and they were passed to secondary units like 7.SS-Gebirgsdivision "Florian Geyer" in the Balkans and to 27.SS-Panzerdivision in France. The Pz.Kpfw. III fought to the last day of the Reich, though only small numbers were left available. For example, the Panzerdivision "Müncheberg", formed in February 1945, had a sole Pz.Kpfw. III Ausf. M in its rank, and there were two Pz.Kpfw. III Ausf. N and one Ausf. M in service with the 23.SS-Panzergrenadierdivision "Nederland". Both divisions perished during the fight in and around Berlin. Finally, on 10th May 1945, the last unit equipped with Pz.Kpfw. III, Panzerbrigade "Norwegen", surrendered to the British forces in Norway.

Soviet soldiers inspect an Ausf. L. The spaced armor introduced to this version is missing, as the counter-balance weight fitted to the gun in the interior was not available at the beginning of production. All hatches are open indicating that the crew was able to escape.

An Ausf. A negotiates a ditch, demonstrating its cross country mobility on a training area. Test tracks like this were mainly used to instruct drivers. The Ausf. A had five large road wheels with individual coil springs, and two large return rollers per side, making it very unique looking from the rest of the Pz.Kpfw. III variants.

A Pz.Kpfw. III Ausf. A during a demonstration exercise, negotiates an obstacle. In May 1937, five of the Ausf. A became available, a further batch of ten vehicles were built until the end of 1937. The armament consisted of a 3.7cm KwK L/46.5 main gun, two 7.92mm MG34 machine guns as secondary armament mounted coaxially in the gun mantlet, and a further MG34 in a ball bearing mount in the front plate of the superstructure.

This obscure photo shows a prototype of the Pz.Kpfw. III Ausf. B towing a second one. Situation like this was performed as often as possible to discover the limits of the tank design. Compared to the clear running gear of the Ausf. A, the eight small wheels design was a step back. This vehicle shows a simulation turret.

A Pz.Kpfw. IV Ausf. D climbing a pioneer bridge. The awkward eight-wheel running gear is clearly visible here. The multiple leaf suspension, cast cupola and extended rear upper tailplate were special features of the Ausf. D.

A Pz.Kpfw. III Ausf. B, presumably of 1.Panzerdivision, followed by several Pz.Kpfw. II, in France. This version introduced a change in the suspension, which consisted of a bogie/leaf spring combination. There were two leaf springs, each supporting two identical bogie trucks, which had four small road wheels each, and three return rollers per side, with the drive sprocket at the front and idler at the rear. Only 15 vehicles were built. (Archiv Trojca)

An Ausf. D moving at speed through the woods during the Polish campaign. The vehicle shows a white cross on the glacis plate which has been disguised.

A Pz.Kpfw. III Ausf. E receiving the panzer gray RAL 7021 paint over the previously used Buntanstrich (early camouflage of gray, brown and green) during the summer of 1939, presumably at the compound of Panzerregiment 1 of 1.Panzerdivision. (via Ledwoch)

Several Pz.Kpfw. III Ausf. E on parade in front of the parliament in Vienna, to the cheers of the populace in 1938 during the German occupation of Austria. The armament consisted of a 3.7cm KwK L/46.5 plus three 7.92mm MG34. (Dr. La Speranza)

A pair of Pz.Kpfw. III Ausf. E on parade, the Balkenkreuz national insignia is painted below the white tactical number 113 on the rear plate of the turret. The Ausf. E was powered by the Maybach HL 120TR engine, delivering 300 PS, the combat weight was 19,500kg, and the maximum achievable speed was 40km/hr. (Archiv Trojca)

A cheerful crowd and a rather happy crew of this Pz.Kpfw. III Ausf. D of 1.Panzerdivision in March 1939 during the invasion of "Rest-Czechoslovakia" (Boehmen und Maehren). After action in Norway with the Pz.Abt. zbV. 40 (Tank Detachment for Special Employment 40), the Ausf. D were transferred to Finland and slowly withdrawn from front-line service. (Archiv Trojca)

The crew of this Pz.Kpfw. III Ausf. E fording a river in France seems to enjoy the ride. The vehicle, which has white turret numbers, is followed by a leichter Einheits-Pkw (Kfz. 1). (Archiv Schnellbacher)

A Pz.Kpfw. III Ausf. E entering a destroyed village during the advance through the Weygand Line in the French campaign. The white 200 on the turret is barely visible. A total of 96 vehicles were produced from December 1938 to October 1939. (Archiv Jerchel)

This Ausf. E waiting for action has been thoroughly camouflaged. The small gun is clearly visible. A weak point of this early version was the internal mounted gun mantlet which could be penetrated easily.

A Pz.Kpfw. III Ausf. E damaged by artillery fire near Erquinvillers in France. The battle damage was shown in good detail. The left side track was separated but the vehicle would soon be repaired and put back into action. (Dr. La Speranza)

Rear view of a Pz.Kpfw. III Ausf. E, presumably of 2.Panzerdivision in France, 1940. Of note are the jerry cans on the engine deck, and the markings on the turret rear. As of May 1940, 348 Pz.Kpfw. III, mostly Ausf. E and F, equipped seven Panzer divisions that saw combat in the Western Front. (Archiv Schnellbacher)

French prisoners of war march past a column of Pz.Kpfw. III Ausf. E. Note the smoke candles mounted on the starboard muffler. (Dr. La Speranza)

A Pz.Kpfw. III Ausf. E going through heavy terrain, offering a nice overhead view. All Ausf. E came off the production line mounting the 3.7cm gun. But from August 1940 till 1942, many were converted to mount the 5cm KwK L/42 gun with an external mantlet. (Archiv Schnellbacher)

Seen during the the invasion of Greece in 1941, this Pz.Kpfw. III Ausf. E overtakes Greek prisoners of war. (Dr. La Speranza)

A Pz.Kpfw. III Ausf. E during the early stage of Operation "Barbarossa", alongside a Horch 830 BL (Kfz. 12) towing a Sd.Anh. 32 trailer. The invasion of Russia began on 22nd June 1941 and Germany amassed 3,200 tanks for this operation, of which 1,440 were Pz.Kpfw. III. (Archiv Trojca)

A retouched (censored) photograph of Pz.Kpfw. III Ausf. E on the march in Russia. The censor has deleted the two machine guns in the mantlet, to the right of the main gun. A mittler gl. Einheits-Pkw (Kfz. 11) ambulance car follows, with another Ausf. E (also censored) bringing up the rear. (Archiv Schnellbacher)

15

An Ausf. F crossing a pontoon bridge (Brueckengeraet B) during the Blitzkrieg in France. A Fliegersichttuch (aircraft recognition device) has been draped over the turret. The Ausf. F was basically the same vehicle as the Ausf. E with changes made to the ignition system. Cast air-intakes were added to the upper hull plate and later models up-gunned to the 5cm KwK L/42 with external gun mantlet. (Archiv Schnellbacher)

It was common for the infantry to take any chance to hitch a ride, in this case an Ausf. E is used as a battle taxi. The soldiers seemed to be in high spirit, as was the case during the early phases of the war. The smoke candles are loaded. (Archiv Trojca)

A Pz.Kpfw. III Ausf. F during the French campaign with spare tracks added to the front of the glacis and the superstructure front plate for enhanced armor protection. (Archiv Schnellbacher)

An Ausf. F on a rather battered looking road during the French campaign, a Fliegersichttuch covers a large section of the turret roof. The engine of the Ausf. F was changed to the 300hp Maybach HL 120TRM, a modified version of the HL 120TR. (Archiv Trojca)

A Pz.Kpfw. III Ausf. F during an exercise on 5th December 1940 at Yargoviste. The turret number 733 appears as outlines only in yellow. The suspension system is evident in this photo, consisting of six road wheels individually supported by torsion bars, with drive sprocket in the front and idler in the rear. Note the escape hatch on the side of the hull. (Motor-Technica-Museum)

An Ausf. F of 4.Panzerdivision advancing south of St. Quentin in June 1940. The divisional insignia, which can be seen on the turret rear, was only used during the French campaign. (Archiv Schnellbacher)

Pz.Kpfw. III Ausf. F with rather large turret numbers denoting 8th company, with the company commander's vehicle in the foreground. (Archiv Schnellbacher)

An Ausf. F of 5.Panzerdivision crossing a Brueckengeraet B pontoon bridge near Lamia in Greece in April 1941. Note the collapsed bridge in the background. (Dr. La Speranza)

Pz.Kpfw. III Ausf. F of 5.Panzerdivision at Kalamata in late April 1941. The vehicles favored large rear stowage boxes and stacked high with supplies. (Dr. La Speranza)

The tank crew of a Pz.Kpfw. III Ausf. F of 5.Panzerdivision in May 1941 posing with infantry soldiers after the rather quick defeat of the Greek Army and the British Expeditionary Corps. (Dr. La Speranza)

A reworked Pz.Kpfw. III Ausf. F with a thin coat of white winter camouflage on the Eastern Front in 1942. The crew are preparing the vehicle for another operation. The Ausf. F were up-armored at the hull and superstructure with 30mm plates, at the same time when the up-gunning to 5cm KwK L/42 took place. (Archiv Trojca)

A pair of Ausf. F advances to the front. Infantry squads often used tanks as transport vehicles, while they could provide cover for the tanks against enemy infantry actions. The last 100 Ausf. F built were mounted the 5cm KwK L/42 gun, and most of the older vehicles were retro-fitted with this gun during overhauls. (via Robert Michulec)

This Ausf. F is retrofitted with the 5cm KwK gun. The vehicle shows bolted-on extra armor on the hull's front, and welded-on plates at the superstructure front. The tactical marking of the 10.Panzerdivision is visible to the right of the driver's visor.

A Pz.Kpfw. III Ausf. G during a field exercise. While early production models of the Pz.Kpfw. III series mounted the standard 3.7cm anti-tank gun as used by infantry units, combat experience soon showed that the 3.7cm gun was inadequate for field use. By late 1940 the short barreled 5cm evolved. (National Archives)

The Pz.Kpfw. III medium tanks had a five-man crew. These included the tank commander, gunner, loader, driver, and assistant driver who operated the hull-mounted machine gun and radio. Crew of this Ausf. G emerge out of the hatches for a breather. (Patton Museum)

Pz.Kpfw. III Ausf. G on a Sonderanhaenger (Sd.Anh.) 116 tank transport trailer, towed by a Sd.Kfz. 8 twelve ton tractor. This tractor/trailer combination was widely used to transport tanks between the front and maintenance depots.

A column of Pz.Kpfw. III Ausf. G, overtaken by a 3-ton Opel Blitz S-Typ (4 x 2) truck followed by a motorcycle, on the move during the Balkans war in 1941. The first fifty Ausf. G were equipped with the 3.7cm gun while the rest had the 5cm KwK L/42 gun with external mantlet. But by late 1942 most early production Ausf. G had been retro-fitted with the 5cm gun. (Archiv Trojca)

A Pz.Kpfw. III Ausf. G of the 11.Panzerdivision, known as "Gespensterdivision" (ghost division), advances pass a knocked out field gun in Yugoslavia during the Balkans war in April 1941. The field workshop often installed a frame to hold equipment and supplies on the rear engine deck. (Archiv Trojca)

A Pz.Kpfw. III Ausf. G of the 11.Panzerdivision passing a knocked out BT-7. The division's personal emblem, a ghost brandishing a sword and followed by speeding tracks, can be barely seen to the left of the Balkenkreuz. Of note are the stick hand grenades hanging at the turret side. (Archiv Trojca)

A close-up of an Ausf. G mounted with the 5cm KwK L/42. The driver's visor was modified as shown, offering better protection. A lot of extra tracks are fitted to the front to reinforce the armor.

This Ausf. G is being repaired in the field. A portal jib helps to remove the superstructure including the turret.

An early Ausf. G during the winter of 1941, with white sheets on the turret for provisional winter camouflage. By late 1941, all Pz.Kpfw. III with the 3.7cm KwK had been phased out of Russia, they were to be converted to mount the 5cm KwK L/42 gun. (Dr. La Speranza)

Photographed in Russia, these Pz.Kpfw. III slowly advance in a village. The vehicle in front is an Ausf. G, followed by an Ausf. J. The tanks were provided with crates and other equipment.

The front drive sprocket with round holes is seen clearly in this photo of an Ausf. G being unloaded from a ship in North Africa. The stowage racks for jerry cans were fitted to tanks of the Panzerregiment 5 for operations in the desert. The three evenly-spaced return rollers and six sets of dual road wheels can also be seen. Ausf. A through G also featured a narrow track only 36cm wide, to be replaced by a 40cm wide track beginning with the Ausf. H model. (National Archives)

An Ausf. G of the Deutsche Afrika Korps (DAK), with a double-layer of spare tracks attached to the vehicle's hull front for added protection. The Ausf. G achieved good success during the early operations in North Africa, but as war progressed, the 5cm-armed Pz.Kpfw. III had to give way to the 7.5cm-armed variants. (Archiv Trojca)

An early Ausf. G of DAK making its way through the North African desert near Tobruk. Due to the intense heat, the crew preferred to ride in the open. Note the amount of jerry cans carried for water and fuel. The battles for Tobruk was the high tide for the DAK, the Pz.Kpfw. III helped Rommel to earn his Field Marshal baton. (Archiv Trojca)

Infantry of the DAK riding on a Pz.Kpfw. III Ausf. G during an attack. Of note are the boots partly made of fabric and used in the early stage of the North African campaign only. Vehicles destined to serve with the Afrika Korps, designated Pz.Kpfw. III Ausf. G (Tp, i.e. Tropen), received an improved cooling air flow by the provision of two cooling air intakes on the rear engine access hatches and better air filters. This version also introduced the ventilator covers on the engine deck hatches. (Archiv Trojca)

A Pz.Kpfw. III Ausf. G of 21.Panzerdivision with British prisoners of war, of note are the PSP of British origin, the spare tracks and the additional spare road wheel fitted to the upper rear plate. The 21.Panzerdivision had its name restyled from the 5.Leicht Afrika Division in August 1941. (Archiv Trojca)

A rare photograph of a Pz.Kpfw. III Ausf G with Schachtellaufwerk, which was fitted for trial purposes but did not enter series production. The vehicle standing to the right is an Ausf. F, the one to the front left is an Ausf. J. (Beiersdorf)

A brand new Ausf. H. This version was introduced in the beginning of October 1940 and a little more than 400 vehicles were built. The hull and superstructure were fitted with factory applied add-on armor, which gave an armor protection of 60mm in total. At the driver's station, a KFF 2 optic was built-in. The rear plate of the turret was redesigned as one piece, deleting the bulge below the commander's hatch

Many Ausf. F through H saw service in North Africa. This Ausf. H is seen passing a destroyed British Matilda infantry support tank in North Africa. The Matilda was more heavily armored than the Pz.Kpfw. III Ausf. F through H. On the negative side the Matilda was slower and mechanically unreliable. (National Archives)

A Pz.Kpfw. III Ausf. H of Panzerregiment 8/15. Panzerdivision during a sandstorm in the desert. The jerry cans marked with white crosses contain drinking water. (Beiersdorf)

A Pz.Kpfw. III Ausf. H moving at high speed in North Africa. These cloud of dust could betray the tank's movement, especially to enemy air reconnaissance. (Patton Museum)

An Ausf. H of 3.Panzerdivision knocked out during the battle in the Smolensk pocket in July 1941. The two color tactical number 531 is well visible in this photo, and the divisional insignia is shown on the front plate of the superstructure. Also noticeable are two penetrations on the front plate that probably destroyed the tank. The panzers of 3rd Panzer Group and 2nd Panzer Group trapped a large Soviet force in the Smolensk pocket in the last week of July that included 300,000 Red Army soldiers and 3,000 tanks. (via Robert Michulec)

A Pz.Kpfw. III Ausf H of 5.Panzerdivision in August 1941 in Potsdam, receiving maintenance by a crew member. The chassis number 66557 appears in white on the upper rear plate. The turret number on the turret rear is in red, with white thin outlines. (Dr. La Speranza)

This Pz.Kpfw. III Ausf. H was photographed during a patrol in a Russian village in February 1942. The tank is overpainted with winter whitewash camouflage. Note the turret stowage box with cutaway sides to clear the rear turret pistol ports. (via Robert Michulec)

Giving a ride to fellow infantrymen, this Pz.Kpfw. III Ausf. H is seen during action somewhere in Russia. The Ausf. H had the chassis modified, including the new 40cm wide tracks which replaced the 36cm wide tracks used on previous versions, new sprockets and idler wheels were also fitted, as were reshaped shock absorbers. The first return rollers were repositioned slightly forward towards the bow as indicated in this photo. (Archiv Trojca)

A Pz.Kpfw. III Ausf. J advancing cautiously through a town in Russia, presumably Minsk. For the first time, this version included an external storage rack on the turret as standard equipment. (Archiv Trojca)

An Ausf. J passes by escaping Russian peasants. The vehicle is camouflaged with scruffy winter wash. The Ausf. J were built from March 1941 until July 1942, incorporating improvements and changes based on combat experience. While the Pz.Kpfw. III Ausf. J early still retained the 5cm KwK38 L/42 main gun, the Pz.Kpfw. III Ausf. J late built from December 1941 onwards received the 5cm KwK39 L/60 gun. Since the rounds of the new gun were longer, the number carried had to be reduced from 99 to 84.

A Pz.Kpfw. III Ausf. J entering a Russian village. The vehicle has a winter whitewash. Note that the entire right forward section of the fender had been lost. The fenders of a tank are easily bent and sometimes get lost when the tank hits an obstacle. (via Ledwoch)

Excellent top view of an Pz.Kpfw. III Ausf. J (early), showing the rearranged and lengthened engine deck. The Ausf. J hull was lengthened, and the rear of the vehicle was redesigned, including the engine deck which received an extension to the rear. (Archiv Schnellbacher)

Following close behind is a Pz.Kpfw. III which, although having the lengthened chassis/hull of the Ausf. J, has a flush engine deck. (Archiv Schnellbacher)

Two Pz.Kpfw. III Ausf. J with improvised winter camouflage applied, standing at the ready in a small Russian village. The whitewash wore off quickly giving the tanks a patchy appearance. (Archiv Trojca)

Getting ready for combat among German infantry, this Ausf. J seems to have the same flush engine deck noticed previously. (Archiv Schnellbacher)

The winter whitewash on this Ausf. J is nearly worn-off completely. The new ball mount is clearly visible. Beginning with the Ausf. J, the hull was simplified, showing new towing loops incorporated to the hull side plates.

Showing severe damages, this early Ausf. J waits for repair in a muddy compound. A wooden jib stands ready for action. The engineers, however, do not seem to be motivated.

Inst.Komp. 194 (engineer company) celebrates its 1,000th repaired tank. In Charkow a great maintenance and repair facility was situated. This early Ausf. J has been decorated, not camouflaged.

Pz.Kpfw. III Ausf. J on flatbed railway cars, for the "convenience" of the crews, tents have been erected behind the tanks. (Archiv Trojca)

A Pz.Kpfw. III Ausf. J (late), recognizable by the late style engine deck, of 24.Panzerdivision during transport by rail. The sections of a tent have been draped over the turret. (M. Foedrowitz)

This Ausf. J clearly shows the right hull lateral escape hatch. The fact that every crew member had an escape hatch could be essential in an emergency after a destructive hit. These hatches were deleted in later versions.

Another Ausf. J with the 5cm KwK39 L/60 of the same unit and on the same train. The turret number 534 seems to be in yellow, outlined in white. The long-barreled 5cm KwK L/60 Ausf. J were first issued to five infantry divisions in early 1942. The rest of the Ausf. J were used to replenish the high losses sustained in both North Africa and Russia. (M. Foedrowitz)

Happy troops hitching a ride on an Ausf. J of 24.Panzerdivision in Russia. The division sign on the starboard fender is clearly visible. Spare tracks were attached to the hull in great extent to somewhat offset the deadly punch of the Russian anti-tank guns. (Patton Museum)

Panzerkampfwagen II and III (latter Ausf. J) lining up in a Russian village, awaiting the order to move ahead. (via Ledwoch)

The Pz.Kpfw. III Ausf. J had the 37mm thick vision port flaps in the mantlet replaced by 50mm armored ones. This vehicle has one of the flaps in the open position. Note the steel helmets hanging over the spare tracks attached to the turret. (Archiv Trojca)

Pz.Kpfw. III Ausf. J in the fortress city Sevastopol which von Manstein's 11th Army secured in July 1942 after a long siege. Both have been camouflaged with bands of sand yellow. Late in the May 1944, a last minute refusal by Hitler to evacuate the Crimea resulted in 64,700 men trapped in the Sevastopol pocket where 26,700 were left behind. (Archiv Trojca)

An Ausf. J with the long barreled 5cm KwK L/60. Although much better than the L/42, the performance was still not sufficient when dealing with Soviet armor. In North Africa, this version was called Mk.III special by the British.

Pz.Kpfw. III Ausf. F, Pz.Rgt. 1, 1. Panzerdivision, River Maas, May 1940

Panzerkampfwagen III Ausführung F (Sd.Kfz. 141) of 2.Kompanie/Panzerregiment 1/1.Panzerdivision , as part of "Panzergruppe von Kleist", spearheaded the breakthrough (together with Infantry Regiment "Grossdeutschland") to the river Maas, crossing it in and around Sedan and the tank battle at Bulson and near Stonne during the "Blitzkrieg" in France, on 13 May 1940. For aircraft recognition purposes, a Fliegersichttuch has been draped over the engine deck of the panzer gray (dunkelgrau RAL 7021) painted vehicle. The company had various versions of the Pz.Kpfw. III at its disposal, including the Ausf. A.

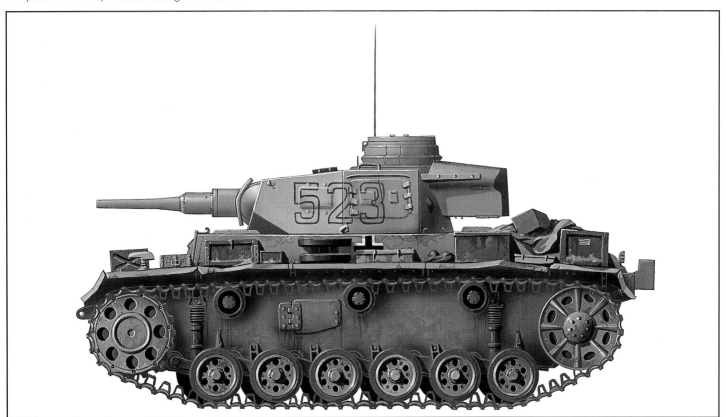

Pz.Kpfw. III Ausf. G, 5.Pz.Rgt., 5.Leichte Afrika Division, El Alamein, June 1941

Panzerkampfwagen III Ausführung G (Sd.Kfz. 141) of Panzerregiment 5/5.Leichte Afrika Division (mot. trop.) near Fort Capuzzo and Halfaya Pass (El Alamein) in defense against the Allied offensive "Operation Battleaxe" in the middle of June 1941. This early version has the early style drive sprockets/idler wheels and the cast armored cupola. The tank is painted in afrikagelb color, the turret numbers are shown only as outlines in red. In August 1941, 5.Leichte Afrika Division was changed to 21.Panzerdivision (DAK).

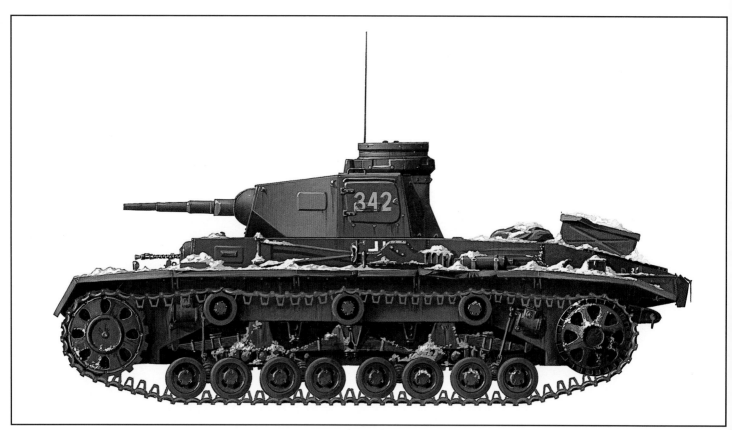

Pz.Kpfw. III Ausf. D, Pz.Abt. zbV. 40, Finland, winter 1941/42

Panzerkampfwagen III Ausführung D of Panzerabteilung zbV. 40 in Finland during the winter 1941/1942. The Abt. (zbV)-40 was attached to Dietl in support of the German landing in Norway and was later transferred to Finland. In 1943 the unit became part of II Abt./Panzerregiment 9 of 25.Panzerdivision. The vehicle is painted in panzer gray (RAL 7021) and has yellow turret numbers.

Pz.Kpfw. III Ausf. H, Pz.Rgt. 8, 15.Panzerdivision, Tobruk, June 1942

Panzerkampfwagen III Ausführung H of Panzerregiment 8/15.Panzerdivision during the battle for Tobruk, which fell to the DAK on 21st June 1942. The vehicle has the new drive sprockets/idler wheels together with the new 40cm wide tracks and is painted in afrikagelb color especially invented to be used with DAK. Due to the quite brutal African sun and permanent move in the desert sand, the color very soon faded away and was worn off rapidly. Whereas Panzerregiment 5 used the full three digits for the turret number, Panzerregiment 8 more than often only used single numbers.

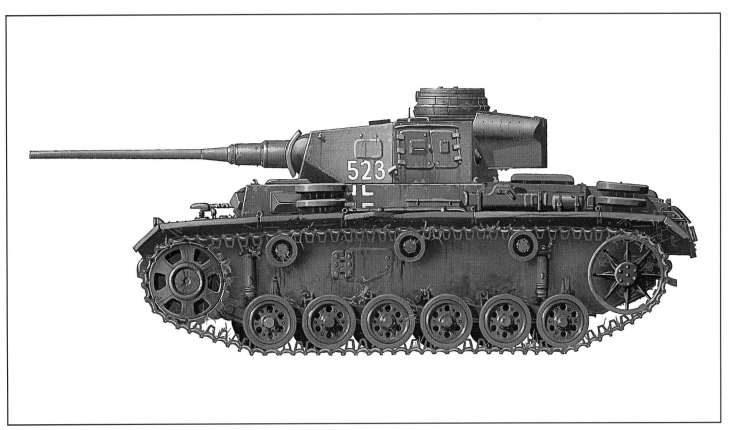

Pz.Kpfw. III Ausf. J, 24.Panzerdivision, Stalingrad, September 1942

Panzerkampfwagen III Ausführung J (late) (Sd.Kfz. 141/1) of 24.Panzerdivision during the battle for Stalingrad in September 1942. The vehicle is painted panzer gray overall and has small white turret numbers. The 5cm KwK39 L/60 gun was very effective against Allied armor in Africa, but proved to be less effective to the well armored T-34. Parts of Stalingrad were taken until November 1942, before the Soviets started a counter offensive during the same month. The bulk of the 24.Panzerdivision (the former 1st Cavalry Division) was lost in February 1943 and surrendered to the overwhelming Soviet forces in Stalingrad.

Pz.Kpfw. III Ausf. N, sPz.Abt. 501, Tunisia, December 1942

Panzerkampfwagen III Ausführung N (early) (Sd.Kfz. 141/2) of schwere Panzerabteilung (sPz.Abt.) 501/"Gruppe Lueder", near Tebourba-Kairouan (Tunisia) in December 1942, where the unit (together with parts of Panzerregiment 7/10.Panzerdivision) took on the US 1st Armored Division. This early version is based on the chassis of the Ausf. L, and it is still painted in afrikagelb, although there is evidence that at a later stage the vehicles were repainted in pea green.

Pz.Kpfw. III Ausf. J, 1.SS-Panzerdivision, Kharkov, March 1943

Panzerkampfwagen III Ausführung J (Sd.Kfz. 141/1) of 1.SS-Panzerdivision "Leibstandarte Adolf Hitler" (LAH) during the fighting around Kharkov-Belgorod ("Manstein Offensive") on 18 March 1943, when Kharkov was recaptured. The tank has an overspray of white winter camouflage applied over the basic panzer gray color, which would soon have to be washed off.

Pz.Kpfw. III Ausf. M, 3.SS-Panzergrenadierdivision, Belgorod, July 1943

Panzerkampfwagen III Ausführung M (Sd.Kfz. 141/1) of 3.SS-Panzergrenadierdivision "Totenkopf" near Belgorod on 2nd July 1943, when the ill-fated Operation "Zitadelle" was launched and the unit attacked towards Oboyan-Kursk. The vehicle is fully equipped with armor skirts (Seitenschürzen) on the chassis and the turret, and has an overspray of green camouflage on the basic sand yellow paint. The turret number in black denotes the 4.Kompanie commander's vehicle.

Pz.Kpfw. III Ausf. M, Pz.Rgt. 11, 6.Panzerdivision, Belgorod, July 1943

Panzerkampfwagen III Ausführung M (Sd.Kfz. 141/1) of Panzerregiment 11/6.Panzerdivision, as part of III.Panzerkorps near Belgorod in July 1943 during Operation "Zitadelle". The vehicle has green (RAL 6003) and red brown (RAL 8017) camouflage patterns sprayed over the basic sand yellow (RAL 7028) color. Commanded by Oberst von Oppeln-Bronikowski during the summer of 1943, most (if not all) tanks of this unit were marked with "Op".

Pz.Kpfw. III Ausf. J, 5.SS-Infanteriedivision, Stalino, August 1943

Panzerkampfwagen III Ausführung J (Sd.Kfz. 141/1) of SS-Panzerabteilung "Wiking"/5.SS-Infanteriedivision (mot.) "Wiking" in very successful defensive operations against heavy Soviet attacks near Stalino in August 1943. The vehicle has a camouflage pattern of green and sand yellow, with the turret numbers shown as white outlines only. The 5.SS-Inf.Div. (mot.) became the 5.SS-Freiwilligen-Panzerdivision "Wiking" on 22nd October 1943.

Pz.Kpfw. III Ausf. N, Pz.Rgt. 11, 6.Panzerdivision, Poltava, August 1943
Panzerkampfwagen III Ausführung N (Sd.Kfz. 141/2) of Panzerregiment 11/6.Panzerdivision, near Poltava in August 1943. After Operation "Zitadelle" had lost momentum, which took the unit as far as Oboyan (to the southeast of Kursk), the unit was forced to retreat to Kirovograd via Belgorod and Poltava. The turret number denotes a vehicle of 7.Kompanie, and varying stripes of green and red brown had been applied to the standard sand yellow basic color.

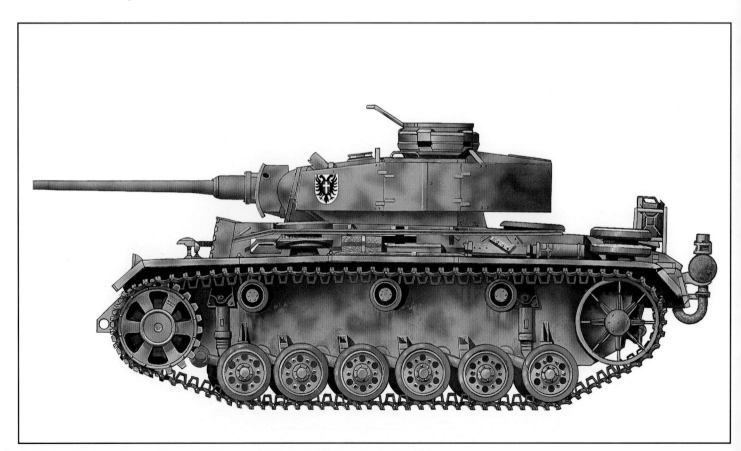

Pz.Kpfw. III Ausf. M, Pz.Rgt. 3, 2.Panzerdivision, Khifzky, August 1943
Panzerkampfwagen III Ausführung M (Sd.Kfz. 141/1) of Panzerregiment 3/2.Panzerdivision (Vienna) near Khifzky, north of Orel in August 1943. The 2.Panzerdivision had most of their soldiers drafted in Austria and had the crest of Vienna applied to many of the division's vehicles, as represented here. This vehicle had no tactical number on the turret.

Pz.Kpfw. III Ausf. M (Fl), 16.Panzerdivision, Salerno, September 1943

Panzerkampfwagen III Ausführung M (Flamm) (Sd.Kfz. 141/3), 16.Panzerdivision in September 1943 during the battles around the Allied beachhead at Salerno. The vehicle shown was one of seven issued to this division and was subsequently captured intact and tested by the US Army. It is painted in sandgelb and has mud applied for camouflage.

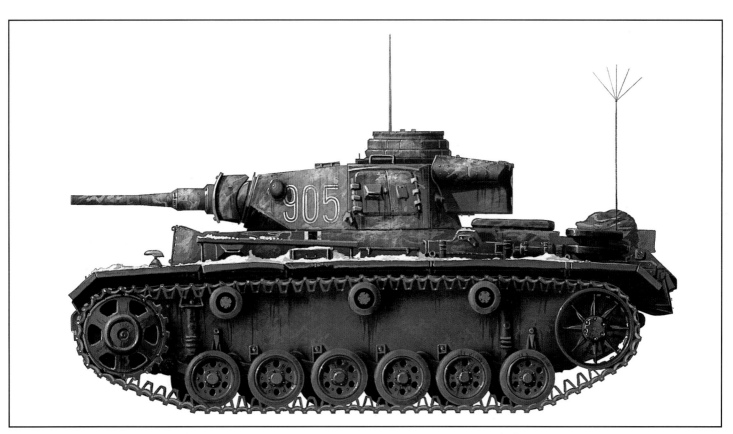

Panzerbefehlswagen III Ausf. K, Pz.Rgt. 11, 6.Panzerdivision, Kirowograd, late 1943

Panzerbefehlswagen III Ausführung K (Sd. Kfz. 267) of Stab II.Abteilung/Panzerregiment 11 of 6.Panzerdivision during the fierce battles around Kirowograd in late 1943. The vehicle has the 2m star antenna for the FuG 8 radio on the rear deck and is armed with the 5cm L/42 gun in a reworked Pz.Kpfw. IV turret. The armored side skirts are missing completely from the vehicle which received a hasty applied winter camouflage over the panzer gray basic color.

Panzerbefehlswagen III Ausf. K, 19.Panzerdivision, Proskurov, March 1944

Panzerbefehlswagen III Ausführung K, presumably of 19.Panzerdivision, on the Eastern Front near Proskurov in March 1944. The vehicle shows the full complement of armor skirts around the turret and on the sides. Panzerbefehlswagen III also served to a certain extend with units having otherwise Pz.Kpfw. IV or Pz.Kpfw. V "Panther". This vehicle is equipped with the long barreled 5cm KwK39 L/60 main gun, and has a disruptive pattern of green and red brown over the basic sand yellow color applied. The Balkenkreuz national insignia on the turret armor is unusual in having an additional yellow cross applied.

Pz.Kpfw. III Ausf. N, Panzerbrigade Norwegen, Norway, May 1945

Panzerkampfwagen III Ausführung N (Sd.Kfz. 141/2), Panzerbrigade "Norwegen", during the surrender to British forces on 10th May 1945 in Norway. Although based on the chassis of an Ausf. M, the gun mantlet was that of an Ausf. J. The vehicle had a full coat of Zimmerit, and was fitted with a complete set of armor skirts. There was no Fliegerbeschussgeraet (MG mount) fitted at the commander's cupola.

Destroyed in battle, this Ausf. J displays its success of previous actions. At least eleven rings were painted on the barrel, an indication of the same number of kills by this tank. In the background a Famo 18-ton halftrack with a track damage waits for recovery.

This Ausf. J of 2.Kompanie/Panzerregiment 8, 15.Panzerdivision, shows its climbing ability. Note the various equipment stowed on the vehicle, in particular the several stick hand grenades hanging down at the side of the turret. (Archiv Trojca)

An Ausf. J with the short 5cm KwK L/42 gun in a staging area. The turret number 143 is in red, outlined white. (via Ledwoch)

One of the Pz.Kpfw. III Ausf. J from Fourth Panzer Army during an attack on enemy position near Voronezh in June 1942, a prelude to the battle of Stalingrad. (via Robert Michulec)

A long barreled Ausf. J idling next to an 88mm flak gun. Note the camouflage colors on the commander's cupola, gun barrel and even the jack. The L/60 gun increased the overall length of the vehicle by 2.5 feet. (via Robert Michulec)

A column of Pz.Kpfw. III Ausf. J of 24.Panzerdivision advances to the area of the big bend in the River Don, making its way towards Stalingrad, just 45 miles away. (via Ledwoch)

In this photo, various Pz.Kpfw. III Ausf. J can be seen, presumably of 24.Panzerdivision on the way to Stalingrad, with a Sd.Kfz. 250/3 halftrack watching nearby. (Archiv Trojca)

Several Pz.Kpfw. II, III and IV, and a single Sd.Kfz. 251, of 24.Panzerdivision can be seen here in an assembly area prior to the offensive to take Stalingrad. This frontal view clearly shows the various details of the Pz.Kpfw. III Ausf. J. The Germans crossed the Don in several places on 23rd August 1942 and reached the northern suburbs of Stalingrad. (Archiv Trojca)

An Ausf. J during the offensive around Stalingrad. The soldier in the foreground carries a 50mm mortar GrW 36 on his back. Stalingrad had been a disaster which cost the Germans the 6th Army. (Archiv Trojca)

An Ausf. J of 24.Panzerdivision in Stalingrad. The vehicle seems to have yellow turret numbers (634), outlined in white. The individual vehicle number (4) is repeated on the rear of the stowage bin on the turret. (Archiv Trojca)

A Pz.Kpfw. III Ausf. J in the winter of 1942 on the Eastern Front. At the superstructure front of the Ausf. J, the Fahrersehklappe 50 vision slot replaced the previously used Fahrersehklappe 30, and the square type Kugelblende 30 machine gun mount was replaced by a ball mount Kugelblende 50 as shown here. This series had the armor protection increased to a basic 50mm. (Archiv Trojca)

Seen from behind, this Ausf. J clearly shows the revised rear. A rack had been added on the engine deck, keeping the extra running wheels in place.

An Ausf. J inspects the result of a tank battle. The tank is camouflaged by winter whitewash. The 5cm KwK was able to deal with the T-34, when met by the side or rear.

A Pz.Kpfw. III Ausf. J that received a thorough winter whitewash in Russia. The well applied snow camouflage was effective in concealing the tank against snow covered surroundings. Even the spare tracks were painted white. (Archiv Trojca)

Another Ausf. J with winter whitewash during the winter of 1942 in Russia. The white camouflage was washable and wore off quickly. The troops riding the tank reminded one about the harsh winter conditions in Russia. (Archiv Trojca)

German troops moving across the wide steppes of south Russia during the winter battles of 1942/43. This Ausf. J has a thorough winter whitewash camouflage. Note the national cross painted on the superstructure side. During the various battles in this winter season, which took part between Causasus, Stalingrad and Kharkov, the Soviets lost almost 4,500 tanks while the Germans lost around 2,600. (via Robert Michulec)

Several Pz.Kpfw. III Ausf. J and Ausf. L of 3.SS-Panzergrenadierdivision "Totenkopf" during Operation "Zitadelle" at the Kursk salient in July 1943. The division formed part of the 1st SS Panzer Korps, which played an important role in the great battle of Prokhorovka. In the foreground, the components of a 80mm mortar GrW 34 is carried by its crew. (Archiv Trojca)

A Pz.Kpfw. III Ausf. J of 2.Panzerdivision aiming its gun to the right, ready for combat. The tactical number 631 appears in white on the sides of the superstructure and to the right on the upper rear plate. The dragon motif on the turret side is also recognizable. (Archiv Trojca)

Seen in France, these Ausf. L moves through a town. The vehicles are brand new, proving that the unit was sent for replenishment to the occupied France.

The Pz.Kpfw. III Ausf. L was introduced in 1942, again showing a few improvements. Spaced armor was added to the gun mantlet (which indeed is missing here) and the superstructure's front. The tank shows a third spare wheel on the mud guard, Rail transport was common for German tank units, since fuel was always in short supply.

Here maintenance engineers remove the engine cover of a Pz.Kpfw. III, probably an Ausf. L, in the field. The portal jib shown here was a very effective and versatile tool designed for use with light to medium tanks.

A new Pz.Kpfw. III Ausf. L for the DAK is off loaded from a German freighter in Tripoli. The stowage rack is filled with jerry cans, proving that this tank was prepared for prolonged action in the desert. The travel in the Mediterranean was dangerous, the British sank about 20-25% of all reinforcements.

An Ausf. L during a battle in the desert. Packed tight with extra equipment, the turret is nearly blocked. It was common practice for the commander to ride with open hatch, listening to his headphone and the battle noises simultaneously.

Photographed after a fierce battle, two destroyed Ausf. L are seen close to a lend-lease ex-British Matilda. In the background a T-60 light tank is visible. British equipment was often used in the southern part of the Eastern Front. Note the open escape hatches, indicating that the crew managed to escape from the vehicle. The gun visible at the left vehicle does not belong to the Pz.Kpfw. III, but to a destroyed T-34.

A rather unusual looking Pz.Kpfw. III Ausf. L of the 5.SS-Infanteriedivision (mot.) "Wiking", as it has the shorter barreled 5cm L/42 gun instead of the longer L/60. Note the 20mm spaced armor on the superstructure front and on the gun mantlet. (Archiv Trojca)

Another Ausf. L with the short barreled L/42 gun, this time of Fallschirm-Panzerdivision "Hermann Göring". Note the absence of turret side vision ports. (Archiv Trojca)

On delivery, the early vehicles of the Ausf. L lacked the armor plate on the mantlet, but had the "frame" already attached on the mantlet. The frame was attached to take on the spaced armor plate, increasing the protection here to 57mm in total. At the start of the summer offensive in 1942, there were approximately 600 Pz.Kpfw. III mounting the 5cm KwK L/60 gun available at the Russian front. (Archiv Trojca)

An Ausf. L advancing behind motorcycles with sidecar, also shows the frame attached to the mantlet but the armor plate is still yet to be added. (Motor-Technica-Museum)

An Ausf. L during the preparation for Operation "Zitadelle" in 1943, the biggest armor battle in history. Note that the chassis is clogged with mud, a problem even in the summer seasons in Russia. During the battle of Kursk, the Pz.Kpfw. III tanks were admitted obsolete and not battle worthy. (via Robert Michulec)

An early Ausf. L somewhere in France, with an air identification sheet barely visible on the rear deck. The recoil system of the 5cm KwK39 L/60 gun was changed from a coil spring to a torsion bar counter-balance mechanism, which resulted in a reduction from 84 to 78 rounds in the ammunition stowage when compared to the Ausf. J (late). (Beiersdorf)

A Pz.Kpfw. III Ausf. L, painted in a winter camouflage scheme, in winter of 1943. Improvements to the Ausf. L included altering the air intakes louvres and hatches on the rear deck. The vision ports were deleted from the turret sides. (Beiersdorf)

A Pz.Kpfw. III Ausf. L, presumably in southern France in September 1943. The spaced armor on the superstructure front is very noticeable. The hull escape hatches on both sides were deleted, indicating a late version Ausf. L. (via Ledwoch)

This late Pz.Kpfw. III Ausf. L shows a full establishment with side armor plates. The German cross is painted in black only, the turret number is stenciled in black as well. Camouflage consists of thin dark green lines sprayed over the dark yellow base paint.

This interesting photo shows an Ausf. L retrofitted with side armor plates. The gun mantlet shows no spaced armor, smoke candles are visible at the turret. The hull side skirts have fallen off and unveils the dark yellow base color. The bear emblem of 3.Panzerdivision is visible on the turret armor skirt.

Hitler was always very interested in military technology. At his personal orders the new and more powerful long barrel 5cm KwK39 L/60 gun was mounted on production Ausf. M tanks. The extra length of the long barreled 5cm gun is clearly seen in this line-up of Ausf. M tanks. The Ausf. M were fitted with three smoke candles on either side of the turret. (Patton Museum)

A column of Pz.Kpfw. III awaiting the order to move out. On the right is an Ausf. M with spaced armor added to the gun mantlet and superstructure front. The Ausf. M had the capability to wade water up to 4.5 feet deep. (via Robert Michulec)

A Pz.Kpfw. III Ausf. M with the distinctive exhaust muffler of this version, and the non return valve on top of it. In this case, SS soldiers ride along on the engine deck. Note the amount of spare wheels carried. (Archiv Trojca)

Mounting on an Ausf. M (evident by the Bosch headlight) for an easy ride to the front, this photo was probably taken in the winter of 1942/43. Note the spare track links stored on the turret's roof.

This interesting photo shows two Ausf. M and a "Tiger" Ausf. E transported with a Siebel ferry. The vehicles are finished in plain dark yellow and seem to be brand new in condition. Note the spaced armor, and Bosch blackout headlights mounted on the fenders.

A Pz.Kpfw. III Ausf. M showing a perfect winter whitewash camouflage. Again, infantrymen taking the opportunity for a comfortable ride to the front.

This Ausf. M of 2.SS-Panzerdivision "Das Reich", presumably in Kharkov in March 1943, is fitted out with Ostketten tracks designed for better traction in winter. The three smoke candles mounted on the forward turret side are covered. (Archiv Trojca)

Against the deadly Russian anti-tank guns and to protect against hollow-charge projectiles which were introduced in 1943, skirt armor plates (Seitenschürzen) were fitted to both the hull and the turret of Pz.Kpfw. III Ausf. M, which were subsequently also fitted to numerous Ausf. L. This Ausf. M is seen fighting in a Russian village. (Patton Museum)

This late Ausf. M slowly advances in the Russian steppes. The large exhaust fitted to enhance deep wading capability is clearly visible.

In 1943, prior to the Kursk campaign, many Pz.Kpfw. III were provided with side armor plates. This destroyed Ausf. M shows the emblem of Pz.Rgt. 3/2.Panzerdivision on the turret side. The vehicle to the right is a PzBefWg III Ausf. H (note the dummy 3.7cm gun). The 9m telescopic mast is partly erected.

A Pz.Kpfw. III Ausf. N (early) of schwere Panzerabteilung 501 (sPz.Abt.), mainly equipped with the Pz.Kpfw. VI "Tiger" I, in Bizerta at the end of November 1942. Most Ausf. N of this unit were based on the earlier Ausf. L chassis, they were used to provide close-support for the "Tigers". (Archiv Trojca)

Greetings from brothers-in-arms. A Hungarian Pz.Kpfw. 38(t) from 1st Armored Division meets an Ausf. N in Russia. The Hungarian armored division was smashed during the Soviet offensive at Voronezh in January 1943. The Ausf. N was the final variant of the Pz.Kpfw. III series and remained in production until August 1943. (via Robert Michulec)

Several Ausf. L and Ausf. N in southern France in autumn 1943. Air recognition sheets are carried by all vehicles on the rear deck. The Ausf. N mounted the 7.5cm KwK L/24 gun and based on the Ausf. J, L and M series. There was no spaced armor on the gun mantlet because of the weight of the 7.5cm KwK. (Beiersdorf)

Recognizable in this photo are at least four Ausf. N and three Ausf. L (early) seen during the invasion of southern France in September 1943. The triple smoke candles on each side of the turret was standard for all vehicles of the Ausf. N. Late vehicles received Seitenschürzen (side skirts) on the turret and the hull, and some vehicles received a single piece commander's hatch (coming from the Pz.Kpfw. IV) instead of the two piece hatch. The installation of a Fliegerbeschussgeraet (machine gun mount) on the cupola was optional. (Beiersdorf)

A destroyed Ausf. N inspected by Soviet officers. Note the penetration points on the armor skirts. This late production Ausf. N shows a slovenly applied camouflage scheme of dark brown and dark green sprayed over the dark yellow base.

A lot of Pz.Kpfw. III Ausf. N were produced by converting damaged Ausf. J or L. This is an ex-Ausf. L as evident by the split commander's hatch. The winter whitewashed vehicle fell into a frozen ditch, and was subsequently deserted by its crew.

This Ausf. N was used against the Germans by Czech insurgents towards the end of the war. Destroyed by at least four 7.5cm rounds, it shows only the dark yellow base color.

This late Ausf. N shows the markings of Pz.Rgt. 3/2.Panzerdivision, a double headed eagle. A large wooden crate was attached to the engine deck. Understandably, the turret couldn't be turned to the back limiting combat value.

An Ausf. N in Slovakia late in the war. The vehicle had the Zimmerit anti magnetic mine paste applied. Late in the war, when the vehicles returned to the factories for major overhaul or repair and converted to the Ausf. N, the majority (if not all) were fitted with factory applied Zimmerit anti-magnetic mine paste. (Archiv Trojca)

The high degree of communication was one reason for the success of German panzer forces. Command tanks like this PzBefWg III Ausf. B provided the troops with reliable long-range radio systems. Note the pistol port in the hull machine gun position, the MG34 in the dummy turret mantlet, and the large frame antenna that made up the distinct features of the PzBefWg III. (BL)

Two "Politruks" (political instruction officers), also known as "Kommissar", were taken prisoner of war and brought to the Befehlswagen for interrogation. The command tanks were needed to direct the movement of the panzer formations during battle. (Archiv Trojca)

A PzBefWg III Ausf. E in France, with the frame antenna for the FuG 8 radios installed over the rear deck shown to good advantage. Although the PzBefWg III looked very much like the standard Pz.Kpfw. III tank, the large frame antenna betrayed their role as a command tank. (Archiv Schnellbacher)

A PzBefWg III Ausf. H of the 4th Panzerdivision in a French town. The only armament carried is one machine gun in a ball mount in the mantlet, to the right of the dummy gun barrel, and a machine gun in the front of the superstructure. (Archiv Schnellbacher)

A PzBefWg III Ausf. H takes the lead of a column of Pz.Kpfw. II during the French campaign. The PzBefWg III Ausf. H had the same hull and suspension as the Pz.Kpfw. III Ausf. H. Early versions had a false mantlet and a dummy gun that simulated the 3.7cm L/46.5 gun, while later versions had the dummy gun installation that resembled the 5cm L/42 gun. (Archiv Trojca)

This close up shot shows the Fahrersehklappe 30 of a PzBefWg III Ausf. H, seen during winter 1941 in the Russia. (Dr. La Speranza)

After a battle, exhausted soldiers take a rest behind a PzBefWg III Ausf. H (late). Early versions were to equip the 17 Panzer divisions on the Eastern Front during the summer offensive in 1941. Later versions mainly equipped the new units such as 25.Panzerdivision and 2.SS-Panzergrenadierdivision. (Archiv Trojca)

An Ausf. J loaded with infantrymen speeds pass a PzBefWg III Ausf. H. This version of the command tank entered service in 1941. A total of 175 vehicles were built, a lot were lost on the Eastern Front.

Here a PzBefWg III Ausf. H, marked with a red cross flag, provides armored cover for wounded soldiers brought to the spot by a Sd.Kfz. 251 Ambulance. (Archiv Trojca)

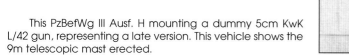

This PzBefWg III Ausf. H mounting a dummy 5cm KwK L/42 gun, representing a late version. This vehicle shows the 9m telescopic mast erected.

Another late PzBefWg III Ausf. H in the winter of 1942/43. This vehicle was not camouflaged, making it easily recognizable in the winter terrain. Both antennae are erected. Note the slit covers added to the headlights.

This PzBefWg III Ausf. H was assigned to 18.Panzerdivision and was converted for diving. The water tight covers of the air inlets are visible. The sealing of the turret ring, however, was not fitted since the turret was fixed. The frame antenna was typical for all command vehicles of this period.

In early 1943 a number of Ausf. J were converted to command tanks. Designated PzBefWg III Ausf. J, they had the same equipment as the latter Ausf. K. The star antenna d mounted on the engine deck is not visible in this photo, the antenna mount on the left side carries a 2m rod antenna. Protection was reinforced by spaced armor on the hull front and the gun mantlet.

A PzBefWg III Ausf. J negotiating a water obstacle. From March to September 1943, 104 PzKpfw. III with 5cm KwK L/42 were converted to PzBefWg III. Note the elimination of the hull machine gun. The ammunition rack was also removed to give way to the long range radio. (via Robert Michulec)

This rare picture shows a PzBefWg Ausf. J. This vehicle had the original 5cm KwK fitted, and the wireless system fitted to the later Ausf. K command tank. As the turret interior was very cramped, this led to a redesign of Ausf. K's turret and weapon system. The armored antenna mount for the distinctive, but less conspicuous star antenna d is visible between the engine hatches.

The PzBefWg III Ausf. K was the first command tank to be provided with a standard tank gun. The turret proved to be too small and replaced by the turret of a Pz.Kpfw. IV. The 5cm L/60 was shifted to the left, thus creating space for additional radio equipment and map table in the turret. These vehicles carried a less conspicuous star antenna d instead of the frame antenna. (F. Schulz)

When the first German self-propelled artillery units were established, armored artillery observer's vehicles were developed using repaired Pz.Kpfw. III tanks. Extended radio equipment was added and the armament was deleted. This is a derelict PzBeobWg III Ausf. H. The dummy gun, which resembles a 5cm gun, is visible. The Zimmerit was applied by field workshop. (J. Mueller)

The PzBeobWg III was introduced for self-propelled units equipped with "Wespe" and "Hummel". Although a dummy gun was fitted, in the mantlet's center, a machine gun for close defense was mounted. This vehicle had the side skirt support frames but minus the side skirts.

This PzBeobWg III Ausf. H was heavily converted to be integrated in Pz.Kpfw. IV units. The original dummy gun was converted with a larger wooden beam and a muzzle brake so that the tank would resemble the 7.5cm KwK armed Pz.Kpfw. IV. Here a Soviet soldier holds the wooden tubing which fell off after the vehicle was destroyed by a mine. Zimmerit and a full set of side skirts were added in a field workshop. This vehicle was destroyed in Kursk in the summer of 1943. (S. Netrebenko)

A Tauchpanzer III Ausf. F diving tank during a test run at Sylt in autumn 1940, being lifted into the water by a crane with all watertight covers in place. The Tauchpanzer III was a submersible wading tank developed in mid-1940 for the planned Operation "Seeloewe" (Sea Lion), the invasion of England. (Archiv Randolph Kugler)

Another Tauchpanzer III Ausf. F. The engine air intakes were fitted with locking covers, and the exhaust was fitted with non return valves. Quite obviously, the flexible air supply hose is attached to a special opening in the turret roof. (Archiv Randolf Kugler)

A Tauchpanzer III Ausf. F going down a special ramp just entering the water. The air supply hose is attached to an opening to the right and in front of the sealed commander's cupola. Note the non return valves on the two exhaust stacks. (Archiv Randolf Kugler)

This Tauchpanzer III Ausf. F is preparing for submerging operation. The cupola, gun mantlet and hull machine gun were sealed with waterproof fabric covers. This wading tank could ford water up to 3 feet without special preparations, and submerge up to 49.2 feet deep. (Archiv Randolf Kugler)

At the outer end of the air supply hose, a float and an air inlet stack was attached. This one seen here is shown on a Tauchpanzer III in operation, still lacking the radio antenna which was later added to enable radio communication with the submerged tank. (Archiv Randolf Kugler)

The flexible air supply hose rests on special holds attached to the vehicle, a Tauchpanzer III Ausf. F, being prepared for a submerging operation. (Archiv Randolf Kugler)

Quite interestingly, this Tauchpanzer III Ausf. F has the flexible air supply hose attached to an opening on the engine deck. Seen in background is the "Viper", a former gunboat, fitted with a special ramp to bring the submerging tanks into water. The large frame attached to this Tauchpanzer III is for test purposes only. (Archiv Randolf Kugler)

A Tauchpanzer III Ausf. F during submerging trials at Hoernum/Sylt in 1940. The air inlet stack on the float, which rests on the rear deck, is fitted with an antenna added to allow radio communication with the submerged tank. (Archiv Wenck)

This well known shot shows a unit of 18.Panzerdivision practicing. As far as it is known, no Tauchpanzer III was ever used for combat diving operations except during exercises.

After being attached to various Panzerdivisions, and being used as deep wading tanks in one occasion by 18.Panzerdivision crossing the river Bug, the Tauchpanzer III were used as regular tanks. This Ausf. G or H, with the seals on the air intakes in place and the attachment frame for the rubber seal around the mantlet fitted, was badly damaged during a fight in Russia.

This Tauchpanzer III was photographed shortly after action in late 1941. The sealing frames around the gun mantlet and the bow machine gun are visible. A lot of extra equipment is packed on the vehicle.

This Tauchpanzer III lacks the perforated sealing frame around the gun mantlet. Possibly this was done due to the fact that diving operations were unlikely after 1941.

This rear view of a Tauchpanzer III shows the redesigned exhaust, similar to that of the Ausf. M. The two snorkel valves are missing, a silencer was not fitted. Interestingly enough, the German cross was carried on a metal sheet.

A Tauchpanzer III Ausf. G waits for action. It is fitted with the 5cm KwK L/42 and has the engine air intakes raised to allow better cooling. All sealing are visible.

Captured by the Soviets, this Tauchpanzer III Ausf. G shows some interesting features. Although the old fashioned drive sprocket and idler wheel are still fitted, a Bosch headlight was added during depot repair work. Behind the commander's cupola a mast is visible, possibly the shortened snorkel.

This impressive shot shows a street in Königsberg, East Prussia, after invaded by the Red Army. A variety of destroyed or abandoned vehicles litter the roadside. In the center a Bergepanzer III fitted with Ostketten is seen. This vehicle shows an unusual modification, apparently a heavy machine gun, possibly a Soviet 14.5mm, was mounted behind an improvised armor plate.

This interesting photo shows a special purpose vehicle, a "Leitpanzer für Ladungsleger" (explosives-carrier). This vehicle has an armored box attached to the turret's rear containing the wireless equipment. The antenna is barely visible. Based on an Ausf. J, this vehicle belonged to Versuchs Kommando (FL) Tropen. Since the climatic conditions were not favorable, the unit was not used in combat.

Frontal view of one of five Sturmgeschütz (StuG III) "O-series" built under use of the 2/ZW chassis, which were used for trial and training purposes only. The two round access hatches in the front hull distinguish this prototype vehicle. (Archiv Trojca)

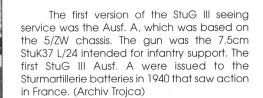

The first version of the StuG III seeing service was the Ausf. A, which was based on the 5/ZW chassis. The gun was the 7.5cm StuK37 L/24 intended for infantry support. The first StuG III Ausf. A were issued to the Sturmartillerie batteries in 1940 that saw action in France. (Archiv Trojca)

The StuG III Ausf. C had a new superstructure design, the main changes being the elimination of the direct vision port for the gunner's sight, redesigning of the roof gunner's hatch, and different armor layout at the front. The Ausf. D looked almost identical to Ausf. C, with a number of vehicles having the armored pannier to the right side of the superstructure as commander's vehicles. (Archiv Trojca)

The major change in the StuG III Ausf. E was the addition of an armored pannier on the right side of the superstructure. Both the left and right panniers were longer than earlier variants, as seen in this Ausf. E with both antennae erected while fighting in Russia. (Archiv Trojca)

Two StuG III Ausf. F (with 7.5cm KwK40 L/43) standing at the ready. The Ausf. F were an effective anti-tank vehicle, capable of destroying the Russian KV-1 and T-34 tanks. Late Ausf. F, thirty one of them, were fitted with the L/48 gun. (Archiv Trojca)

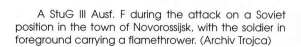

A StuG III Ausf. F during the attack on a Soviet position in the town of Novorossijsk, with the soldier in foreground carrying a flamethrower. (Archiv Trojca)

A StuG III Ausf. F/8, which was based on the longer 8/ZW chassis derived from the Pz.Kpfw. III Ausf. J. The Ausf. F/8 was mounted with the L/48 gun and had the additional 30mm armor bolted to the front of the hull and superstructure. During 1942, the demand of the StuG was so great that production of the Pz.Kpfw. III ceased and concentrated on the StuG III. (Archiv Trojca)

The StuG III Ausf. G (early) retained the hull of the Ausf. F/8, but had modifications recognizable by the early form of the additional armor around the driver's visor, and a design change to the superstructure with a cupola added to the commander's hatch. This Ausf. G is seen on the Eastern Front in 1943. Note the Notek light in the center of the hull front. (Archiv Trojca)

A pair of StuG III Ausf. G in the Russian steppes. As evident by the 2m rod antennae the vehicle in the foreground is a command vehicle. Both are brand new vehicles of the mid production lot, showing smoke candle dischargers and the box-like gun mantlet. Neither camouflage nor markings are evident. Condition is excellent, parts of the side armor skirts, however, have fallen off. It is of interest that a half plate was added for increased protection of the crew. (W. Schneider)

This StuG III Ausf. G has the Zimmerit anti magnetic mine paste applied, and has the side skirts fitted. The Ausf. G mounted the same 7.5cm StuK40 L/48 gun as the Ausf. F/8. Late production vehicles featured the Saukopf gun mantlet, coaxial machine gun, the Nahverteidigungswaffe (close-in defense weapon) and remote-control machine gun at the roof. (Archiv Trojca)

A snow-camouflaged StuG III Ausf. G during an assault on the Eastern Front in 1944, followed closely by infantry. The Sturmgeschütz units were often engaged in heavy fighting, many participated in the battle of Kursk in 1943. (Archiv Trojca)

A StuG III Ausf. G during the fights in Warsaw in 1944. The antenna seen mounted to the left hand side denotes a guide vehicle for remote controlled demolition charge carrying vehicles (Funklenkpanzer) and belongs to a Funklenkpanzer unit. (Archiv Trojca)